More Monologues for Teenage Girls

Nagvara

MORE MONOLOGUES
For
TEENAGE GIRLS

Susan Pomerance

Dramaline Publications
36-851 Palm View Road
Rancho Mirage, CA 92270
Web Site: dramaline.com E-mail: drama.line@verizon.net

Library of Congress Cataloging-in-Publication Data

Pomerance, Susan.
More monologues for teenage girls / Susan Pomerance
    p. cm.
Summary: A collection of monologues for teenage girls, exploring such topics as parents, dating, drug abuse, friendship, and sex.
ISBN 0-940669-53-6 (alk. paper)
    I. Monologues—Juvenile literatire. 2. Acting—Juvenile literature. (I. Monologues.] I. Title.
PN2080 P6632 2002
812'.54—dc21   2002023896

ISBN-10: 0-940669-53-6
ISBN-13: 978-0-940669-53-6

Cover art by John Sabel

This book is printed on paper that meets the requirements of the American Standard of Permanence of paper for printed library material.

CONTENTS

KAREN

Her parents' bickering has gone too far. After taking it as much as humanly possible, Karen finally admonishes them severely for their constant harangue:

Do you two realize you argue constantly? It seems it's all you ever do. It never stops. Do you realize, do you have any idea how much you're ragging on each other? And you don't solve anything. Nothing. Day after day it's the same old argument over stupid little things and money and who's right and who's wrong. And nothing ever gets solved. Anyway, who cares who's right or wrong? Is right and wrong the end of the world? Is "right" more important than happiness? Sometimes I wonder why you ever got married in the first place.

And how do you think it affects Kerry and me to hear you screaming at each other day after day? You think we can't hear you? You think we're deaf, or something? We hear you in the kitchen in the morning and in your bedroom at night. Sometimes I cover my head with my pillow so I won't have to hear you yelling and swearing like a couple of crazies. And you argue in front of us, too.

1

Let me ask you, do you have any respect for each other at all? Is there any love left? Even a bit? Was there ever? When you look back, can you see yourselves as you used to be back when you cared and had respect, before something, God only knows what, got between you? Do you ever stop to remember the good times, what it was like when you were young? There must have been caring and consideration—something. Now it seems like all the caring is dead. What ever happened?

You not only don't have any respect for each other, you obviously don't give a damn about Kerry and me either. If you did, you'd stop the constant bickering and hatefulness. Either that or just get a divorce and get it over with. As much as I would hate it, it wouldn't be nearly as bad as living like this.

Do me a favor, both of you: Grow up!

SALLY

Her father's temperament fluctuates greatly with his financial fortunes.

My father is, like, two people, you know; Mr. Nice Guy when the stock market's on fire, Mr. Pain-in-the-Butt, when it isn't. Last week, when the Dow went crazy and gained all these points, he was all smiles, going around being super nice to Mom and me. He was even nice to the cat. It was like he was on uppers or something. What he did, he'd bought this energy stock real low and, for some reason or other, it'd doubled in price and he'd made a whole bunch of money. Boy, was he ever pumped. He was walking around like it was Christmas, the Fourth of July, and his birthday all rolled into one. He gave me twenty dollars and took us out to dinner at this restaurant where they had finger bowls. Then he sprung for a movie at the Cineplex. He didn't even complain when I wnet back for seconds of popcorn and Cokes. And on the way home he didn't bitch about my CDs.

Then, yesterday, Dr. Jekyll turns into Mr. Hyde. I was in my room surfing the Net, okay, when, alluva sudden, I hear Dad drop a really loud F Bomb..

When Mom and I go see what's happening, he's sitting in front of his computer with his head in his hands, stamping his feet on the floor like my cousin Harold does when he has one of his ridiculous tantrums. Then he starts screaming at the computer, swearing at is like it's human, or something. What had happened was, the energy stock he bought had taken a dump.

The whole rest of the evening he's in this lousy, grouchy mood, complaining about everything—about how Mom and I don't have any appreciation for money and how we spend too much and how we have no idea what is costs to run the house. Insane.

You know, I think rather than being in the stock market, it makes more sense to just go out and buy stuff.

JUDY

From experience, Judy knows the pitfalls of dating an older man.

(*Noting a photo.*) So, this is the guy, huh? (*Beat.*) What do I think? You really wanna know? Really? Well . . . I think you should stop fooling around with someone ten years older than you, that's what. You're asking for big trouble here. (*Beat.*) Hey! You asked me what I thought, so, I'm telling you. Okay? I'm telling you that getting involved with someone this much older is asking for trouble.

(*Beat.*) What? He loves you? Are you kidding me here? Look, I was involved with this person I met on vacation at the lake last summer. Seven years older. He started calling and we exchanged e-mai and we got involved. Behind my parents' back, of course. (*Beat.*) Why didn't I tell you? If I had, you'd have given me the same advice I'm giving you now, that's why. And I didn't wanna hear it. Anyway, we'd meet on the sly and things got pretty hot and heavy, you know. And it was kinda neat, because it was like this romantic thing out of some book or movie or play or something. It was neat. And I was really totally into the guy. In love, I guess. So I thought at the time, anyway. I was flattered and it was exciting. Being involved with someone this much older made me feel sophisticated and adult.

We met like this for about three or four months, okay? Until, one day, while we're having coffee at Starbuck's, his wife comes in and makes this scene you wouldn't believe. She went ballistic right in front of everybody, screaming and yelling, calling me a little bitch and him worse. It was awful. I was scared. I wanted to run. I didn't know what to do. Hey, I had no idea the guy was married. I'm real lucky she didn't try to call my parents. Wow.

So listen, Janet, take my advice here: Stay away from this guy. Dump him. Fast. (*Noting the photo again.*) Besides, he's a total dork. I mean, nobody wears wing-tip shoes anymore.

DORIS

Doris gives her reasons for not dining in the school cafeteria:

Okay, Sheryl, so I don't eat in the cafeteria, so what? So I have better sense, okay? The caf is always too hot and it smells like sour milk. Besides, I kinda like being alone. In the morning, I throw some stuff in my backpack: a peanut-butter-and-jelly, a turkey san, maybe a Twinkie and a Diet Coke. Then I go over to the park, sit down at a nice bench, and eat. In peace. Nobody around, no screaming and yelling, no bumping trays.

Besides, the cafeteria food sucks big-time. You eat there day after day, your stomach turns to cement. The last time I ate in the caf, the food was so bad I almost barfed. I can't believe some of the slop they throw together. Wow! You ever eat their meatloaf? It's, like, they rip the sole off this old boot and cover it with something that looks like gravy. And I think they must do their mashed potatoes in a blender because you could drink it. Slop, Sheryl, pure slop. And how about their Jell-O? How can anybody screw up Jell-O? But they do. They somehow got ahold of this secret Jell-O-screw-up recipe. And they're always going on to us about the building blocks of nutrition. Building blocks, all right, because the meat they use is as tough as

7

bricks. They also go the exclusive rights to a recipie for Instant Diarrhea.

And the menu never changes. Ever notice? Monday: Swiss steak, French fries, green beans, and Jell-O. Tuesday: spaghetti, coleslaw, garlic bread, and Jell-O. Wednesday: Meatloaf, mashed potatoes, lima beans, and Jell-O. Thursday: Johnny Mazetti, salad, rolls and, Jell-O. Friday: Filet-of-sole, wilted-lettuce, boiled-potatoes and Jell-O. And the stuff's disgusting and all tastes exactly alike. If they ever gave you a blindfold test on it, you'd guess "leftover Alpo."

The cafeteria is totally sick.

JANET

Selecting the "perfect tree" is not always a joyous occasion.

Do your parents get into a big thing every year about your Christmas tree? (*Beat.*) Really? Boy, are you ever lucky. With us it's always a total nightmare. We always get our Christmas tree from this lot over on Main Street. The guy who runs it is this strange dude who has an Adam's apple that's too big for his neck and who eats sunflower seeds and talks at top speed—yada, yada, yada. And he's this super salesman. He sells Mom a bigger tree every year. She always tells Dad she's going to get a smaller one, but every year she comes home with this gigantic bush, ya know.

Last year we go over and the guy shakes out a bunch of trees that are crooked and deformed-looking. Real weeds. And Mom goes bananas because she's a Christmas-tree nut and has to have one that's perfect. And she tells him she wants a *small* tree, okay? A nice, perfect, small tree. Well, it seems as though there aren't any nice, small, perfect trees—only large, perfect trees with tall, imperfect prices.

The tree she bought cost a hundred and fifty bucks and was so big they had to deliver it in a pickup, which cost another

9

twenty-five dollars. When Dad saw it, he couldn't believe she'd bought a twelve-footer, because it meant we had to cut off three feet because our ceilings are only nine feet high. And when he saw the price tag, he turned greener than the needles. She didn't tell him about the delivery charge. This would have ruined his Christmas.

Now get this: The tree trunk was so big around it wouldn't fit in our holder. This meant we had to go out and buy this real expensive stand. Another thirty-six dollars. Boy was Dad ever pissed.

This year he says he's going with Mom to the tree lot, and if the guy tries to con them into anything over six feet, he's going to chill his tinsel. Whatever this means.

DARLENE

Darlene's personal experience justifies the old adage, "You can't tell a book by its cover."

I ride the bus to school almost every day. To pass the time, I usually read or do my homework or look out the window and daydream, but most of the time it's pretty boring. So yesterday, to keep from getting bored, I decided to try to figure out people by how they looked. Make up stories about them, you know.

Well, across the aisle was this distinguished-looking guy who was wearing these neat suede shoes and a tweed coat. I figured him for a guy who was aristocratic but had to ride the bus because he blew all his inheritance money on cars and jet-set women. I figured him for a Trevor.

The woman next to him had cat hair all over her coat, so I figured her for this eccentric old maid who, when she died, was going to leave a secret fortune to her animals. I got her as an Edith.

A couple of rows up was this young, nerdy-looking guy in dirty chinos who was nose-deep in a book on stamp collecting. Right away I figured him for a guy who spent most of his life

11

in his room and had never been kissed—maybe not even by his own mother. I got him as a Rodney.

The bus driver was big and burly, with wrists on him like bedposts. He never smiled. I got him as an ex-jock who didn't have the smarts to go on to college. I named him Butch.

Sitting in the corner was this creepy-looking guy who kept staring at his feet. He had so many tattoos on his forearms that, at first, I thought he was wearing a long-sleeved sweater. He was a carnival type for sure, probably the dude who bites the heads off chickens. I got him as a Billy-Bob something-or-other.

At my stop, the carnival geek gets off behind me. Kinda spooked me, ya know. But when I dropped a book, he bent over and picked it up and handed it to me and said, "Here you are, Miss." Miss? Hey, was this polite or what? Then he smiled, and when he did, he wasn't so geeky anymore. Maybe his name was Reginald.

Just goes to show: You can't tell jack by looking at a person.

HELEN

Ron is handsome, a girl's dream, but he is also a shallow, duplicitous person. Helen has discovered this and proceeds to make it clear to him in no uncertain terms.

You wanna know why? Because you're a self-centered, egotistical, cheating fool, that's why. (*Beat.*) Yeah. (*Beat.*) So I care? You think I *really* care? Forget it. Not anymore.

I used to think you were special, really something. You could do no wrong. You were perfect. Mr. Everything. This is before I found out you're nothing but a phony, lying, cheating bastard. You pretended to like me, but you really didn't—it was all this big act. I shoulda known better, but I got sucked in by your looks. Big mistake. Now I know what my Mom means when she says looks aren't everything. Hey, I'm beginning to wonder if they mean anything at all.

Why'd you have to dump on me, Ronny? Why? (*Beat.*) What? C'mon, please don't give me that. Don't insult me here, okay? You think I don't know about you and Charlotte Westerfield? (*Beat.*) Yeah, Charlotte "Big Tits" Westerfield. You think I don't know that after you leave me you go over to her place? (*Beat.*) Yeah, Shirley told me. And thank God she did. If she hadn't, I'd still be thinking you could walk on water.

What is it with you? Is it that your self-image has taken over or something? Is it you've talked yourself into believing that you're so special you can treat people like crap? (*Beat.*) Well, let me tell you something, Mr. Knight in Rusted Armor: You may be beautiful, but there's nothing inside. Inside, you're hollow, empty like somebody turned you upside down and poured out all the character. You're a shallow, nothing person, Ron.

You hurt me, but I'll get over it, it'll pass, I'll find somebody else. But you? You're stuck with yourself. Too bad, because "yourself" is a rotten partner.

DIANE

*Although she and Jenny are best friends, Diane will not leave
her home town for big-city life.*

You do what you want, okay? I'm staying here in Springdale.
(*Beat.*) Yeah, so what? So it's not sophisticated. I'm not interested in sophisticated; I'm more into sanity and not swimming
upstream against a zillion people. (*Beat.*) Well . . . that's your
thing, you've always been into big and fast and loud. This is
you, Jen. Like the stereo you put in your Civic. The bass
thumps so loud it rattles the windows. Okay. Cool. Like I said,
this is you. And I'm not being critical. We're just, like, these
two totally different people. For me, I want small and quiet and
slow. (*Beat.*) So what, it's not progressive. Hey, what can I tell
ya? I'm not even ready for a cell phone.

Look, remember the last time we were in Manhattan? Well,
for me it was, like . . . like this zoo, you know. Totally. I mean,
oh yeah, it's happening all right, it's got everything, but it's
just too damned crowded and too crazy. (*Beat.*) Two days,
okay? More than this, I'm outta there.

Besides, I don't wanna leave my friends and family and
stuff, start up with new people, a new neighborhood, live in

some ratty little apartment. (*Beat.*) Yeah, okay, I can understand that. I'm not against change. What I'm against here . . . for me, anyway, it would be just changing for the hell of it, you know. For you, good. For me. . . .

Look, Jenny, we've been friends since grade school. You think it's not gonna be lonely around here without you? I'm really gonna miss you, Jen. I mean . . . like you're my very best friend ever, you know. But I wouldn't be happy in Manhattan, any big city. It just isn't me. You? Hey, girl, you got Big City written all over you. And it's all you've talked about all through high school. You *should* get away. Hey, you'd go crazy here.

Anyway, I'll come visit you. (*Beat.*) Sure, sure I will. I'll stay with you and we can shop and hang out and go out at night and get jostled.

ROBERTA

She can no longer endure expectations of perfection.

. . . Oh yes you do. Absolutely. You criticize every word I say, every move I make. Why? Why do you need to point out every little mistake I make, or, I should say, every little mistake you *think* I make? Okay, all right, so I said ain't. Big deal. As if it's all that important. Ain't is criminal? For "ain't" I get life without parole? Like yesterday at Sharon's when I didn't put a coaster under my Coke. Like I thought you were gonna freak for sure. You realize how embarrassing this was for me, being treated like some child, or something, corrected in front of evryone? You have any idea how you yelled at me in front of all those people? I'll never forget the look on Sharon's face. She couldn't believe it.

Let me ask you something, Danny: What makes you so extra- special? What makes you so much better than everybody else, puts you above them? What gives you the right to set yourself up as judge and jury about almost everything? You have any idea how critical and negative you are? No, I don't think you do. And this is the sad part. You really *do* think you're superior, special, above people.

17

Well, hey, I can't take it anymore. I'm burnt out with it. Totally bummed. I just can't take being constantly uptight about how I dress and look, talk, my manners—*everything*.

I really like you, Danny, I really do, but I also like myself too much to continue to put up with your put-downs. I'm not perfect. I have flaws. I have problems. I make mistakes. I say, ain't. Every now and then I even pick up the wrong fork. I goof up in public sometimes. You know what this is called, Danny? Do you? It's called being human. *Human.* You're a smart guy, Danny, and you know a lot about stuff, but I've had it. Give me a call sometime when you learn how not to be a smart-ass.

ELLIE

Ellie, suspicious of her father, has followed him and discovered him with another woman. Sickened and angry, she confronts him regarding his infidelity.

Okay, all right, that's enough. You're being ridiculous. So stop! Stop it with your lies here, okay? I know what's happening, so your feeble, lying explanations and stupid excuses won't work. I know the truth.

(*Beat.*) Oh, yeah? (*Beat.*) Think? Think? Are you kidding? I don't give a damn what you or anybody else thinks. And I'm not keeping my voice down. If the people in the restaurant hear, they hear, okay? Screw them. Think? Why weren't you concerned what the people who'd be affected would think, about their feelings? Did you think about me, Sally . . . Mom? Oh no, hell no. Your slut was bigger than that. Thank God I was suspicious. Thank God I saw you with that woman.

I had a feeling, the way you'd been acting lately: indifferent, in a daze, not coming home till all hours. And poor Mom. Poor, trusting Mom. Believing in you, loving you. And how do you repay this? By cheating on her with some young slut. (*Beat.*) What? How *dare* you defend that woman to me. Do you have

19

any shame, for God's sake? Any? Don't you realize what you've done, what this is going to mean? Do you have any regard at all for the people who are going to be hurt?

(*Pushing him away.*) No! No! Don't touch me. Don't come near me. Get away from me because I hate you. How the hell could you do this to my mother? Us? It's, like, driving a stake though the heart of your family. You loser. You bastard! You inconsiderate, cheating bastard.

(*Beat.*) Yes, you're damned right I followed you. And, boy, am I ever glad I did. How long have your secrets and lies been going on, Dad? How long? You bastard. (*Beat.*) How can I talk to you like this? You kidding? It's easy—you deserve it. The hard part will be telling Mom.

ALMA

Alma, late for soccer practice, has forgotten her sweats. Her coach has rummaged through a box of discarded items and given her a pair of yellow pedal-pushers. She is appalled at the thought of wearing them.

Ewww! I can't wear these things. Puleeze. Yellow pedal pushers? C'mon. The team will freak. And what if Ralph sees me in these. Oh, man. He'll dump me for sure. I wouldn't blame him. Has the coach totally lost his focus or something? Or maybe it's his sick way of getting even with me for forgetting my sweats. He's like that, you know. He cut the toes out of Amy Martinez's socks when she forgot her shoes.

Ewww! Just look at these things. I look like 1958. (*Beat.*) Yeah, sure, easy for you to say. Would you wear these? Would you be caught dead in 'em? (*Beat.*) Okay, I rest my case.

(*Beat.*) Retro? C'mon with retro. These aren't retro, Molly, they're puke-o. And look where they hit me. This is *not* a flattering length. And how about baggy. (*Pulling out the waistband.*) I could throw my cat in here. Man, these are awful. I wonder where these came from. Musta been around here since the school was founded.

21

Coach Harris has gotta be out of his mind. I don't think he likes me anyhow, you know. He's had it in for me ever since I blew that soccer ball past his darling daughter. Pampered bitch. You ever catch the way he treats her? "Honey" this, "Princess" that. Does this wanna make you puke or what? She shouldn't even be on the team. A total spaz. If she wasn't Harris's kid, she'd be in a home.

I'm not wearing these. No way. No chance. He can kick me off the team if he wants. Whatever. Besides, I don't play well unless I'm styling.

MISTY

In rehab, recovering from drug abuse, she tells her counselor of the travails of her days of use and dealing.

It's, like, I never thought I'd ever get addicted, you know. I guess you never do. It never occurred to me I'd get into the drug thing. I didn't even smoke. Then one night my boyfriend and I go to this rave party and do some X. I was instantly hooked. So was he. After this, all I cared about were my new druggie friends and partying.

I wasn't living at home anymore. I'd moved in with my boyfriend after my parents split up. Even though we had jobs, it was really rough for us to make ends meet, because we were spending all our money on X. So we decided to start dealing. We worked out a deal with this supplier we'd met at one of the parties. He was a steady connection and kept us well-stocked because we paid him on time.

Things were cool for a while. Bitchin'. We were making plenty of cash and living good. We were careful and only sold to people we knew. Then, one night, one of our good customers introduced us to this guy, and we sell him forty hits. He was young and seemed cool. Turns out he's an undercover cop.

23

Well, we were arrested and booked and I was in jail for three days before my dad bailed me out. It was awful. It was totally embarrassing for me and my family. And I didn't have any of my old friends anymore because they didn't hang with drug users. I was all alone. It was a really down time, and some days I was so depressed I couldn't get out of bed.

I had to go to court and it cost my dad a lot of money. They let me off with community service and house arrest and I have to see you every week.

Things are pretty cool between me and my dad, but my mother won't speak to me. But I'm coming back. Slowly but surely I'm getting it together. I'm feeling good. I'm clean and I'm gonna stay clean. I have a life ahead of me and I'm not gonna blow it.

MARLENE

She understands that relying on one's natural gifts is useless unless combined with hard work and dedication.

Hey, no wonder your parents are pissed. Can you blame them? Like, c'mon. With all the talent you have? Look, Sue, you're one of the smartest kids in school, okay? Maybe *the* smartest. You're super intelligent, everybody knows this. You're a brain. You don't even take books home and you still get by. Me? I gotta crack books every night and work my buns off to maintain Bs. For me, school has never been easy; it's an uphill thing. But for you—a breeze. But getting Cs? Like, this is outrageous.

I can't blame your father. If I was your dad, I'd take your car away, too. (*Beat.*) Too strict? Are you kidding? Whadda you expect? He realizes you're blowing your future, maybe blowing college because you're lazy. (*Beat.*) Hey, okay, if this is you attitude, fine. But don't come bitching to me, okay? If you can't see the light, you can't see the logic, this is your problem. Don't come complaining about losing your car, crying around about losing your allowance and that. Like you asked for it, okay? If I was your dad, I'd ground you for a month. Make you sit in your room till you got your head outta your buns. (*Beat.*) Yeah, right, I would. And not because you bring home some Cs but because of your lazy, don't-give-a-damn attitude.

You know what? As long as we're leveling here, I just gotta tell you this, Sue: You know why I'm the only friend you have in school? It's because nobody else can get past your arrogant behavior. I know you're smart, everyone knows you're smart, but what pisses people off is that *you* know it. And it shows. You go around wearing your smartness on your sleeve. But know what? Getting Cs because you're lazy and losing friends because you're arrogant isn't being smart, it's being really dumb.

STACY

Stacy, a victim of dating violence, tells her boyfriend that their relationship is over.

(*Pushing him away.*) Stay away from me, okay? Get the hell away from me, creep. You think after what you did last night I'll have anything more to do with you? Are you kidding? What the hell's wrong with you, anyway? Is this what girls are to you—sluts? Are we all sluts? Huh? Someone to be shoved around? I was warned about you, but I didn't believe it. I guess I was just fooled by your looks. When I first saw you, I said, "Oh, wow!" 'cause you looked outrageous, you know. Yeah, you're outrageous, all right.

(*Her hands up as a barrier.*) Stay away from me, I said. Back off! Don't come any closer. (*Beat.*) You know what you are? You're a nut case, that's what. Some kinda psycho who gets off on abusing girls.

I wonder what makes a guy like you tick. I wonder what goes on inside the mind of someone like you. Is it that you hate girls, women, or is it, for some screwed-up, sick reason or other, you hate yourself?

27

You realize what you did to me? Here, take a look, big man. (*She pulls up her sweater sleeve, exposing a large bruise.*) Isn't this beautiful? Huh? Isn't this just lovely? And I've got another bruise on my shoulder. God, if I hadn't jumped outta the car, who knows what you woulda done? I'll never forget the look in your eyes. Thank God I got away. And just because I said, "No." "No," apparently a word you've never ever heard before in your messed-up, screwed-up life.

You're damned lucky I'm not going to the police. I could, you know. I got every right. Maybe I will. It might save some other poor girl from getting pounded, or maybe worse. So stay away from me. Far away.

I guess this goes to show that you really never know. You go out with someone you think is special and you wind up with an animal.

JUDY

Judy describes to a friend the realities of being a teen parent:

Oh, man, if you only knew. Having a baby is really, really hard. You got no idea, Linda. When I get home in the evening, I got to do my homework, feed him, give him a bath, get him to sleep and get myself ready for bed. And I got to get up with him during the night and then get up real early in the morning and get myself ready for school. My mom watches him during the day, and this is really a drag for her, you know. I mean, like, she's not young, she had her babies. Now here she is, starting all over. I feel sorry for her, but until I graduate, I don't know what else to do.

You know what really bums me? It's when another girl finds out I have a baby and thinks it's cool. She has no idea. Hey, a car is cool, a new outfit is cool, new shoes; a baby is not. They take all kinds of attention and work. And it's constant. When you become a mom, you become totally responsible, you know. And for the rest of your life. You can forget about your weekends and summer vacations and all that because your child will always be there. It not like you can say,

"Okay, I'm tired of being a mother," and just give up. The child's still there. It's a living, breathing thing.

I had a good relationship with Jerry before I got pregnant. We were tight. Every day he told me he loved me. But after, it was as though I didn't exist. I called him after the baby was born and said, "You have a son." He was like, "No, I don't. *You* have a son." Jerry went on his merry way.

Linda, whatever you do, don't mess up like I did. It changes your whole life. For, like, maybe five minutes of pleasure you get a lifetime of responsibility. If I'd been better informed, I'd never had sex in the first place.

GINGER

Her parents, recently killed in a car accident, were not only abusive alcoholics, they were also unfeeling with regard to their inheritance. But Ginger has no illusions, carries no guilt for her feelings of resentment toward them.

Okay, I know it sounds harsh and disrespectful, I know it sounds awful. But you know what? I *mean* to be harsh. I mean to be harsh because I have to be honest with myself and not blow myself a bunch of smoke just because they were my mother and father. Harsh is exactly what they deserve. Better, really, for the terrible parents they were, for the way they mistreated me. Damn them! Damn my mother and father. Respect gets what it deserves.

Look, my parents weren't exactly the All-American mother and father. To be honest, they were All-American losers. They treated me like hell. They made my life miserable from the time I was born. You have no idea. Me and my sister, Janet, they treated us both like hell. We never felt any love. They pushed us around, neglected us, forced work on us, and when they were drinking they were downright abusive. When my old man got boozed up, he took liberties, if you know what I mean. They have names for people like him.

My parents screwed us in life and screwed us over in their will, too. Left everything to Tony, our older, kiss-ass brother. He was their favorite. Could walk on water. Why? Who knows. Sometimes Janet and I think we were adopted. Tony wound up with the house, the cabin, cars . . . you name it, he got it all. Well over a million. Janet and I? All we got is what we'd gotten from them since birth—*nothing*. They were cold, unfeeling, drunken losers. I hated them so much that one day I drove out to Sunset Memorial and spit on their graves.

Sorry, but this is how I feel.

CAROLE

Carole has come to the realization that her father has AIDS. The tragedy is exacerbated by the fact she hadn't been told, and also hadn't been told that he had left her mother for another man.

You shouldn't have kept it from me, Mother. You should have been up front right away. Why didn't you, right from the start, tell me Dad was gay and that he left you for some guy? But you covered it up, kept me in the dark.

I knew you guys weren't getting along because you argued a lot and you didn't show any affection for each other, any warmth. You think I was too young to notice? (*Beat.*) Oh, yeah, then why'd you go into this big charade about him feeling bottled up and not being happy and not feeling free and all that? And Dad, he tells me the same thing. A lot of double-talk and avoiding. Lies, all lies. What is it with you two, anyway? I'm so innocent and naïve I can't handle the truth? Hey, you know what you were trying to feed me? Birds and Bees crap, that's what, silly old-timey sex stuff because of your old-school attitudes.

What am I here, a baby? I'm not living today or something? I gotta be protected? I've never heard the words *gay* or *fag* or *dyke* or *homosexual*? I never heard the F-word? Get real. You think I couldn't deal with the fact my father was gay? You think I'd freak? Gimme a huge break. Anyway, I figured out for myself what was happening.

After Dad left, I ran into him at Adriano's having lunch with this man who certainly wouldn't qualify as a dock worker, you know what I mean? They were real chummy. I suspected something right then, but when I ask you, you go into total denial. And then, when he started being sick and losing weight and I asked you what was happening, you still skirted the issue. Hell, why didn't you just come out and tell me he had AIDS? It's no disgrace. The disgrace is that you didn't tell me in the beginning. If I'd known early on, I could have spent more time with him, time we'll never get back because he's dying. Why'd you guys have to lie?

SELMA

Selma discovers that her new love interest is a phony.

When I'm back in Ohio this summer, at the mall looking at styles, sorting through a rack of trash, out of the corner of my eye I see this guy sitting in a chair playing air guitar. Real handsome, Sue, beautiful. Like I figure his girlfriend's in the dressing room, right? Well, it turns out she isn't—he's alone sharpening up his chops. Weird, though, I thought, practicing fingering in the girls' department of Macy's. But . . . hey! So, anyway, I go in the dressing room and try on this outfit and come out and check myself out in the three-way mirror. I gotta say, Sue, I looked pretty hot.

This guy apparently thinks so too, because he goes, like, "Wow!" I go, "Pardon me?" like I'm put off and kind of pissed at his comment to make him think I'm cool. Then he goes, "Sorry, but I just had to say something 'cause you're totally outrageous in that dress. I didn't mean to be rude." Well, of course, this shed a whole new light on the situation, you know. I mean, not only is the guy a God, he's mannerly, too. So we talk and stuff and when I ask him about his air guitar, he tells me he's with this major rock band from Cincinnati. I'm completely impressed. Who wouldn't be? When I ask him why he's practicing in the girls' department, he tells me it's because he can check out his moves in the three-way mirror, that it gives him a better perspective. Well, one thing leads to another, and I agree to meet him that night for dinner and a movie. Why not? If you'd seen him. . . .

But thank God I ran into my old girlfriend in the cosmetics department. When I told her what had happened, she broke up good. I guess it's, like, this guy's thing, his way of picking up dates. She knows him from her English class. She told me he's a total phony and that he doesn't play air guitar or any guitar. All he wanted to play was me.

DANA

Dana and her date have been driving around for hours because he can't make up his mind where to eat. She is hungry and fed up with not being fed.

Look . . . know what? I really don't care. Chinese is cool. Italian is cool. German is cool. Mexican is sensational. Sushi is wonderful. I would die for kosher. At this point, I really don't care what kind of food it is. Even a greasy hamburger would be beautiful. A double-bacon-cheeseburger, blood-rare on a soggy bun—even this will do. Even though I don't eat meat very often, even though it gives me diarrhea, I don't care. I'm so hungry I could eat the knobs off your car radio.

We've been driving around now for over two hours. It's almost ten o'clock. So I think it's about time you made up your mind where we're going to eat. We go in this Japanese place, and you don't like the look of the waitress—dirty fingernails. So we get up and leave. Then we walk out of Roma Italiano because they seated us too close to the kitchen. Hey, right now I wish I was *in* the kitchen. Then we drive all the way to Riverdale to the Chez Montmartre. And here you really freak because the guy at the next table said there was fur in his rabbit. This is ridiculous. Besides, you didn't have to order rabbit.

You could have ordered something else. Like what about the French fries? You can't go wrong with French fries in a French restaurant. And French fries are totally furless.

Then we drive all the way back to Roma Italiano, where you get into a big thing with the maitre d' because there's an hour wait. What'd you expect? If we'd stayed put the first time, we'd be full of pasta and belching our way to a movie instead of driving around in circles with our bellies kissing our spines.

Stop! Stop the car! Pull over! There's a McDonald's.

PAULA

Paula was seated nearby when fellow students were gunned down by a disgruntled ex-janitor. Here she describes the incident to a reporter:

None of us knew anything about him. He was just this guy who was around. We only saw him every now and then. He worked in maintenance. He'd come into the room maybe six, seven times a year to replace lights or readjust the thermostat or make some minor repair, or something. He was always very quiet, never said a word, didn't speak to anybody. He just came in and did his thing and left.

It was just terrible. Terrible. The whole thing was just . . . it's beyond description. You can't come close to describing the horror of something like this. You're in total shock and your mind's kinda rejecting what's going on. Maybe it's, like, how nature protects us in situations like this. Like how shock kills pain. All I know is, it was bizarre. And it all happened so fast, it seemed. In a bunch of flashes, like passing pictures. Here we are, doing our work, when, alluva sudden, he bursts in and starts shooting. There wasn't anything anyone could do. It was on top of you before you could think or react or anything. Besides, we were frozen with fear.

He went about the thing in this . . . this very cool manner. This was the far-out part of it, how calm the dude was about killing. I think this is the part that sticks with me the most, you know.

And the killings weren't random. He knew what he wanted to do. First he killed two people in the principal's office and then came in our room and shot certain kids at their desks. He was, like, picking and choosing. I've never been so scared. Hey, maybe I was next. Who knew?

He had a bunch of guns. Three, at least. Maybe more. The guy was a walking arsenal, reloading as he went. It was a nightmare. The girl at the desk next to me, Shirley Grimes, she was gunned down where she sat. Horrible. When he turned toward me, I was sure this was the end. But he passed me over. Why? Who knows? It was just an insane, crazy thing.

ISABEL

Isabel and William, who haven't seen each other since he moved across town, have a chance meeting. A once dowdy, overweight intellectual, she has transformed herself emotionally as well as physically. Here she brings William up to date about herself:

Yes, I was pretty standoffish, I guess. Shy. I used to be pretty much of a stay-at-home. I did a lot of reading. Reading was my way of avoiding people, the fact I was unpopular, the fact I had a weight problem. I always had this arm-load of books with me, remember? Stacks. I lived inside of books—fantasized. I remember how I would have died to have been Daisy in *The Great Gatsby.*

I fancied myself this intellectual who knew more than anybody else. Oh, I was smart all right, but what it really was, was that I was totally ashamed of my weight, and, for that reason, I hid behind my smarts and stayed away from people—especially boys. You know I only had one date last year? With Billy Creamer. Remember him? The real skinny guy with bad teeth and thick glasses who looks like he's in pain all the time? God, he was even more dorky than I was. If that was possible. For our date we sat in his car and discussed Shake-speare's sonnets. This was as sexy as it got.

Then, one day while trying to squeeze my size-fourteen bod into a size eight, I decided enough was enough. So I stopped pigging out and went on a diet of no junk food, more vegetables, and less smarts. And I started exercising. With getting thinner and not working at being an intellectual boor, I started feeling better about myself and I started dating normal people and having a lot more fun. Looking back now . . . (*She shudders at the memory.*) Ugh. I was a mess.

(*Beat.*) Huh? (*Beat.*) You would? Yeah. Sure. Saturday at seven's fine. I'll look forward to it. (*Beat.*) Okay, I'll see you then. And I promise not to bring my copy of *War and Peace*.

KRISTAL

Kristal holds back nothing in this tirade against her greedy, uncaring, older sister.

Okay, stop it! (*Beat.*) Stop it, I said! That's enough! Good God, Helen, what is it with you, anyway? Here Mom's in the next room dying and you go bringing up money and wills and who's gonna get what. Do you ever think about anyone but yourself? Ever? Right now what's going on isn't about *you* or any damned will, it's about my mother, *your* mother.

It seems like your concerns are always more important than anything, you know that? (*Beat.*) Like hell. You've always been a self-centered bitch who puts herself before everyone and everything. Everybody knows this. Look, I may be your baby sister, but I'm a helluva lot older than you in a lotta ways. You have any idea how immature you are, how shallow? No, I don't think you do because it's impossible for you to give any consideration to anything that doesn't put you at the center.

Well, you aren't at the center of this. Your mother, who's full of cancer, in pain, lying there in the next room dying, is totally more important right now than your grubby concerns or anything else. Who the hell cares who gets money? Who gives a damn who gets the house? The fact you can even bring this stuff up at a time like this. . . . You know what you are, Helen? You're a totally cold, uncaring, greedy bitch. (*Beat.*) Oh, yeah? I'll talk to you any way I want.

You walked away years ago, didn't even have the decency to say good-bye. You broke Mom's heart. Now you waltz back in because you think there's money in it for you. Well, forget it, bug off! I've seen the will. You get zip. You get what you are—a zero!

ZELDA

Zelda realizes the life-altering consequences of sex.

I know, but how do you think it would be after? If I put out, then what? It wouldn't be the same between us, you know that, don't you? It would totally alter stuff. It just has to. Right now you respect me, but what about after? Would you look at me the same, treat me the same way you do now? Would there still be respect? Maybe, but I don't think so. Maybe not from me either. I'd be the same person and all, yeah, but a part of me would be gone, missing. And this is something you don't ever get back.

Some of my friends have gotten into serious sex and they tell me, if they had it to do over, they'd never have done it because it changes things, alters stuff, the way you behave to each other. They say, even though it's pretty neat, it takes away something nice.

I'm just not ready, you know. Like I have goals and things I don't wanna throw away. What if I get pregnant? My life would be totally different. I wouldn't be free. And what about you? Would you hang around? Do you wanna be tied down with a baby? There's just too much to lose. I wanna go to college, and then after college I want a career.

This doesn't mean I don't like you, not at all. You know I love you. You're the coolest guy I've ever known. But as much as I care for you, I care about myself more. I hope this doesn't sound self-centered and bitchy, but I just don't think a few minutes of sex is worth the risk, that's all. I hope you understand, because I want us to be together, I don't wanna break up. So please don't keep pushing me, okay? The answer is no.

PEGGY

She speaks of the realities of living in a crime-infested area.

Yeah, I know, but you still have no concept, man. You think you do, but you really don't. You gotta live where I do to know it. You and I are from, like, different planets even though we both live in the same city. The north and south sides are different worlds. In my neighborhood there isn't a lot of money or a lot of hope, just a lot of poverty and people getting through every day the best they can, trying to stay straight and stay out of trouble and not get hurt. But it's not easy, because trouble is all around, you live with it, the drugs and violence and people getting popped. Last week this gang-banger got whacked right across the street from our house. His blood is still on the sidewalk.

We have heavy bars on our windows, all of them. And our front door is steel with little holes in it for air. We're supposed to be free, but we're not—we're just as much prisoners as if we were in jail.

I don't go out at night. No way. Not unless my dad drives me, that is. It's way too dangerous. Even sometimes during the day I feel strange about going on the streets. And when I do, I always watch my back because you just never know. I know this sounds paranoid, but it's better to be paranoid than dead. My little bro, we never let him go out alone. You hardly ever see little kids on the street

Gangs are around. On corners. In lots. The place is crawling with gangsters. Drug deals are happening. I can look out my bedroom window at four in the morning and see people just hangin' around. They aren't out for the air. Cars come and go at all hours. It's a very bad scene.

The neighbors have gotten together and are trying to clean up the place, but so far things are still pretty scary. You've heard people talk about the city being a jungle? Well . . . where we live it is. And the animals have two legs.

CANDICE

Candice has had it with the phony approaches.

Huh? What? Are you kidding? I don't believe this. Well . . . they call me Candy because I'm sooo sweet. Okay? Can't you tell? I'm just this great big mountain of walking sugar. I'm afraid to put my finger in my mouth because I don't want to get diabetes. Instead of using two lumps, I just stick my finger in my coffee. After dinner, I suck my toes for dessert. C'mon, get real here. I'm called Candy because it's short for Candice, you idiot.

What is it with you guys, anyway? I guess you feel you gotta come up with stuff, invent cool junk for an opening line, something you think's cute that'll get a girl's attention and make her think you're something other than a water-brain. You realize how lame this is, how stupid and insulting? If you really wanna get our attention, why don't you come up and say, "Hey, are you really a nympho?" Or, "Do you know if you put salt in your mouth while you're having sex, you won't get pregnant?" How about, "Didn't I meet you once in prison?" This would be totally ridiculous, but at least it'd be creative.

Sometimes I wonder if guys ever give any thought to the way they approach girls. Apparently not. I guess their sense of self-cool gets the best of their brains. I'd die if some new guy would come up to me and say, "Excuse me, my name's so-and-so, and I'd like to get to know you." Boy, would this ever be refreshing.

(*With sarcasm.*) Do they call me Candy because I'm so sweet? Good God.

Get outta here. Bug off.

JEANETTE

Hanna's low self-esteem has lead to degrading, dangerous behavior.

You obviously just don't get the picture here, do you? (*Beat.*) What? What is it with you, anyway? Every time I try to talk sense to you, you go zoning out on me. Okay? You ask me these questions, then, when I try to answer, you go into your trance thing. But not this time. This time you're gonna look at me and listen. This time you're gonna *focus*.

Look, you got this big problem, Hanna, and it's called a total lack of self-esteem. This is why you go around displaying this outrageous, random behavior. You just can't believe guys can accept you for who you are, so you gotta make a spectacle of yourself and go all outrageous. (*Beat.*) The hell you don't. Look at me. In the eyes, Hanna, don't look away.

You actually think this kinda stuff is attractive? Do you? Well, it isn't, it's stupid and a bad way to get attention. Don't look away! Okay, if you think guys are gonna notice you when you do drugs, you're right, they will. How're they gonna ignore you when you're staggering around, slurring your words, a beer in one hand, a cigarette in the other? Yeah, this gets you

51

attention, all the attention you want, but it's sick. You're not only making a fool of yourself, you're also gonna wind up a drugged-out alcoholic slut. Don't look away!

What's the next thing, huh? Do every guy in school so you'll be popular? Another thing: What decent guy's gonna be seriously interested in some slut who has to prove her popularity by putting out and getting wasted?

(*Beat.*) Yeah, sure, you're popular all right. The way you behave, no wonder your cell's always ringing. Problem is, it's ringing for all the wrong reasons.

FRANCINE

Francine, a former gang member, is now outside the situation, has cleaned up her act, is living the straight life. Her social worker has convinced her to speak to a group of her peers about the negative aspects of gang participation.

At first the gang scene looks cool, so you wanna jump in, you know. Things at home are bad, you father's strung out and abusive, your mom's never around. At least the gang's a family. And you make up other reasons too. About school being dangerous so you need cover, protection, and you gotta do what you gotta do . . . fist, blade, or pop gun. And gangs look romantic. So you get involved.

Some gangs are hard to get into, so you gotta do stuff to prove you're cool. I had to go through getting beat up, getting tattooed, taking part in a robbery and having to fight, like, five, six gang members. Some of the gang used their fists and were kicking me, but I remember one homeboy had on brass knuckles that broke my nose. One girl hit me with a stick. I also had to have sex with a bunch of them at the same time. It was scary, but later I felt like I belonged to something, had power and respect. It was very cool. Until I was asked to take part in a drive-by, that is. Then I wanted out. It was getting scary.

But this is the bad part—trying to get out. It isn't that easy. They don't want you out. You know their plans and secrets and what they've done. So when you tell them it's over, they beat you and threaten you. After I dropped out they'd follow me. I became super paranoid, afraid of getting stabbed or shot.

While I was walking to the store with my bro one day, this car filled with gangsters comes outta this alley. My old gang. Two of them shot at me as they drove by. Neither of us was hit, but my bro got scratched pretty bad 'cause I pushed him down hard to get him outta the way. It was awful, but it comes with the show.

They finally decided to let me alone. I was lucky. A lot of my old crew aren't. Sometimes the only way they get out is dead.

CLARE

Although Sarah is her best friend, Clare will not tolerate her reckless behavior behind the wheel.

Pull over, Sarah! Stop the car! Pull over *right now.* (*Beat.*) Why? Why? Because you're outta control, that's why. You're not paying attention and taking care of business. So, *pull over!*

(*Beat.*) Good. Whew! I'll walk the rest of the way. At least I'll get to school in one piece. But before I go, I gotta tell ya, the way you drive, you're gonna crack this thing up bad someday. And what's with not wearing your seatbelt? (*Beat.*) It looks funny? Are you kidding me here? Hey, you're gonna look a whole lot funnier with your head through the windshield after you pile this thing into a tree. You think you woulda learned something from what happened to Amy Clark. She wasn't wearing a seatbelt either if you'll remember. (*Beat.*) C'mon, sure you knew her. She was in our Latin class. (*Beat.*) Right. Blonde, real pretty?

She thought it was tacky to wear a seatbelt, too. But if she had, she'd still be in our Latin class instead of Ferncliff Cemetery. Only sixteen and dead. We're talking tragic. I still can't get it outta my mind about her. The thought of her last few sec-

55

onds on earth really bugs me. Was she afraid? Did she feel pain? Did she think of all the people who loved her? Her parents? (*She shivers.*) She was so pretty and smart, too, had it all happening. But she wasn't smart enough to understand you have to buckle up. And she'd just gotten her own car for her birthday. Too bad she couldn't have enjoyed it longer.

So you better get your crap together and wear your seatbelt and stop driving like a maniac.

I'm outta here. I'll see you at school . . . I hope.

CHARRISE

She resents parental restrictions with regard to dressing, tattooing, and piercing and wrongly views the tastes of small-town America as archaic.

I wanna get a tattoo for my sixteenth birthday and maybe my tongue pierced. But if I do it without my mom's permission, she'll freak for sure. So I gotta wait. I hate getting an adult's okay. It really bums me.

With my mom, everything has to be goodie-two-shoes, and with everything that isn't, she's like, "No, you're not." She's still all stupid skirts and middie blouses and stuff. Everything else she thinks is bizarre. Like the other day when I wore my dark blue jeans and phony snake belt, a long-sleeved magenta shirt and three-inch shoes, you'd thought I'd committed a crime or something. I liked my outfit a lot. But what I like doesn't count. Oh, no. I never get to wear the really cool stuff, stuff that's *me*. It's, like, I gotta check with the clothes police before I leave the house. Lemme ask you, is this any way for a civilized person to live?

I guess this is because Mom grew up on this farm in Indiana. We were back there last summer and it was like the people were from Mars. Total country geeks. I've never seen such random dressing in my life. Ewww! One day, when I wore my flare jeans, silver belt, and my plum sleeveless split-v tank with my fake-leather jacket over it, I thought the local dorks were gonna have a stroke. When I walked into the Wal-Mart, I thought people were gonna lose their eyeballs.

My mom thinks it's better back there because almost none of the kids have tattoos or anything pierced. She says tattoos and piercing make you look like a circus freak. My Mom's pretty neat, but she's out of it—totally Indiana. And her taste in clothes makes me wanna puke.

Soon as I'm legal, I'm getting my belly button and tongue pierced. Then I'm going back to Indiana and scare the locals by hitting the streets totally naked. It'll be, like, this wakeup call to the 21st Century.